The Usborne Big Spotter's Sticker Book

The Usborne Big Spotter's Sticker Book

Jane Chisholm, Phillip Clarke,
Lisa Miles and Anthony Wootton

Designed by
Nayera Everall and Laura Hammonds

Edited by Sarah Khan

Illustrated by
Joyce Bee, Hilary Burn, Trevor Boyer, William Giles,
Christina Howes, Ian Jackson, Aziz Khan, Annabel Milne,
Peter Stebbing, Sue Testar and Phil Weare

Consultants:
Peter Holden, Dr Margaret Rostron and Dr Mark A Spencer

contents

Flowers and plants

Trees

Birds

Insects

Animals

Sticker pages

Flowers
and
Plants

Here are some of the words used to describe parts of a flower:

Buttercup (cut in half)

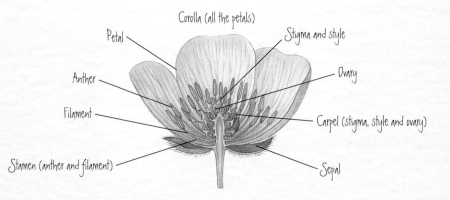

Corolla (all the petals)

Petal

Stigma and style

Anther

Ovary

Filament

Carpel (stigma, style and ovary)

Stamen (anther and filament)

Sepal

The stickers for this section are sticker numbers 1 to 45.
You'll find all the stickers at the back of the book.

White flowers

Cow parsley

Cow parsley

Also called Lady's lace. Ribbed stem. Feathery leaves. Clusters of white flowers. Grows on banks and in ditches. Up to 1m (3¼ft) tall. All summer

WHEN.............................

WHERE.............................

White dead-nettle

Looks like ordinary nettle, but leaves don't sting. Flowers grow on stem. In hedges and on waste ground. 60cm (23½in) tall. Early summer to winter

WHEN.............................

WHERE.............................

Clover

Creeping plant. Each leaf made of three leaflets. 10–25cm (4–10in) tall. Late spring to summer

WHEN.............................

WHERE.............................

Daisy

Daisy

Leaf rosette at base. Name comes from "day's eye", as flowers close at night (and in bad weather). Very common on lawns. 10cm (4in) tall. All year, except mid-winter

WHEN.............................

WHERE.............................

Sea aster

Grows in saltmarshes, which are areas of sand and salty mud. Mauve or white petals. 1m (3¼ft). Late summer

WHEN.............................

WHERE.............................

White dead-nettle

Clover

Sea aster

Yellow flowers

Cowslip

COWSLIP

Single clusters of
nodding flowers.
Rosette of leaves
at base. Grows in
meadows. 15cm (6in)
tall. Early summer

WHEN......................

WHERE.....................

Gorse

GORSE

Dark green, spiny bush.
On heaths and commons.
Flowers smell like almonds.
1–2m (3¼–6½ft) tall.
Spring–summer

WHEN.............................

WHERE.............................

creeping buttercup

Long, trailing stem.
Shiny flowers. Hairy,
deeply divided leaves.
Grows in grassy places.
0.5m (1½ft) tall. Summer

WHEN.............................

WHERE.............................

Creeping buttercup

Dandelion

Very common. Rosette of
leaves. Yellow flowers close
at night. "Clocks" of downy
white parachutes carry seeds.
15cm (6in) tall. Spring–summer

WHEN.............................

WHERE.............................

Bird's foot trefoil

Small, creeping plant.
Flowers streaked with red.
Grassy banks and downs.
10cm (4in) tall. Summer

WHEN.............................

WHERE.............................

Bird's foot trefoil

Dandelion

blue flowers

cornflower

Greyish, downy leaves.
Grows in cornfields and
on waste ground. Fairly
rare growing wild. 40cm
(15¾in) tall. Summer

WHEN...........................

WHERE.........................

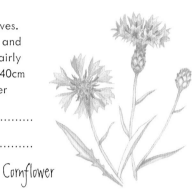

Cornflower

Viper's bugloss

viper's bugloss

Long, narrow leaves. Rough,
hairy stem. Grows straight
up or creeps. Pink buds
become blue flowers.
On waysides and sand
dunes. 30cm (12in) tall.
Summer–autumn

WHEN...........................

WHERE.........................

Bluebell

Clusters of deep violet-
blue flowers. Shiny leaves.
Carpets woods. Spanish
bluebells also seen –
pale blue, pink or white,
with broader leaves.
30cm (12in) tall. Spring
to early summer

WHEN...........................

WHERE.........................

Bluebell

Speedwell

speedwell

Hairy plant. Grows in large
mats over ground. Pinkish-
blue flowers grow on upright
spikes. Leaves grow opposite
each other. Woods and grassy
places. 30cm (12in) tall. Summer

WHEN...........................

WHERE.........................

Sea
holly

sea holly

Stiff, spiny plant. Grey-blue
leaves. Round flower heads.
On sandy and shingle beaches.
50cm (19¾in) tall. Summer

WHEN...........................

WHERE.........................

Purple flowers

Tufted vetch

Long tendrils. Climbs up hedgerows. Brown seed pods in late summer. 0.5–2m (1½–6½ft) tall. Summer–autumn

WHEN.............................

WHERE..........................

Tufted vetch

Common teasel

common teasel

Head made of many tiny flowers. Turns brown and brittle in winter. 70cm (27½in) tall. Summer

WHEN.............................

WHERE..........................

Ivy-leaved toadflax

ivy-leaved toadflax

Weak, slender stalks trail on old walls. Yellow lips on flowers. Shiny leaves. 0.5m (1½ft) tall. Summer–autumn

WHEN.............................

WHERE..........................

Common dog violet

common dog violet

Creeping plant. Rosettes of heart-shaped leaves. Pointed sepals. Grows in woods. 10cm (4in) tall. Spring–summer

WHEN.............................

WHERE..........................

sea lavender

Grows in saltmarshes (areas of sand and salty mud). Leaves have long stalks. Flowers grow in clusters. 30cm (12in) tall. Summer

WHEN.............................

WHERE..........................

Sea lavender

Pink and red flowers

Bell heather

Clusters of bell-shaped flowers. Thin, needle-shaped leaves. Grows on dry heaths and moors. 30cm (12in) tall. Summer

WHEN............................

WHERE............................

Bell heather

Blackberry

Dense, woody plant. Climbs up hedges. Sharp prickles on stems and under leaves. Berries ripe in autumn. 1m (3¼ft) tall. Summer–autumn

WHEN............................

WHERE............................

Blackberry

Greater bindweed

Greater bindweed

Climbs walls and hedges on waste ground. Large, pale pink or white funnel-shaped flowers. Leaves shaped like arrowheads. 3m (10ft) tall. Summer–autumn

WHEN............................

WHERE............................

Ragged robin

Forked stem. Narrow leaves. Flowers have ragged, pink petals. Grows in damp meadows and woods. 30–70cm (12–27½in) tall. Early summer

WHEN............................

WHERE............................

Ragged robin

Soapwort

Clusters of scented flowers. Broad leaves once used to make soap. Grows near rivers and streams. 40cm (15¾in) tall. Late summer to autumn

WHEN............................

WHERE............................

Soapwort

Scarlet pimpernel

Flowers close by mid-afternoon, or in bad weather. Black dots under leaves. 15cm (6in) tall. Summer

WHEN.............................

WHERE.............................

Common poppy

Scarlet pimpernel

Common poppy

Soft flowers with dark middles. Stiff hairs on stems. Round seed pods. Grows in cornfields and waste ground. Up to 60cm (23½in) tall. Summer

WHEN.............................

WHERE.............................

Dog rose

Dog rose

Thorny stems. Grows in hedges and woods. Red rose hips in autumn. Up to 3m (10ft) tall. Mid-summer

WHEN.............................

WHERE.............................

Red campion

Hairy, sticky stem. Pointed, oval leaves grow opposite each other. 60cm (23½in) tall. Early summer

WHEN.............................

WHERE.............................

Red campion

Sea bindweed

Trails along ground, binding sand together. Thick, shiny leaves. 60cm (23½in)

WHEN.............................

WHERE.............................

Sea bindweed

Grasses

Marram grass

Grows on sand dunes. Long roots and leaves trap sand. 1.2m (4ft). Spring–autumn

WHEN.............................

WHERE...........................

Sea couch grass

Marram grass

Sea couch grass

Just above high tide level. Ridges of sand build up around it. 40cm (15¾in). Spring–autumn

WHEN.............................

WHERE...........................

Timothy grass

Flowerheads usually green. Pastures, roadsides and wasteland. Used to make hay for animals. 40–150cm (15¾–59in). Summer

WHEN.............................

WHERE...........................

Timothy grass

Red fescue

Pastures, lawns and marshes near the sea. Very fine leaves. 20–90cm (8–35½in). Summer

WHEN.............................

WHERE...........................

Red fescue

Flowers can be green, purplish or reddish

Common couch grass

Common on farmland and wasteland. Rough, dark, grey-green leaves. 30–120cm (12–47in). Spring–autumn

WHEN.............................

WHERE...........................

Common couch grass

Crops

Wheat

Barley

Wheat

Europe's biggest crop. Mainly used for making bread flour and animal feed. Up to 1m (3¼ft). Late summer–autumn

WHEN............................

WHERE............................

Barley

Grown for beer-making and animal feed. Up to 1m (3¼ft). Summer

Long spikes, called awns

WHEN............................

WHERE............................

Oil-seed rape

Grown for the oil in its seeds. Leftovers used as winter feed for cattle. Bright yellow flowers cover fields. Up to 160cm (63in). Late spring

WHEN............................

WHERE............................

Oil-seed rape

Oats

Will grow on fairly poor soil, without much sunshine. Mostly grown in northern Britain. Used for animal feed and porridge. Up to 120cm (47in). Summer–autumn

WHEN............................

WHERE............................

Sugar beet

Sugar is extracted from the white root, and the leafy tops are fed to animals. Provides about half of Britain's sugar. Up to 1m (3¼ft). Autumn–winter

WHEN............................

WHERE............................

Sugar beet

Oats

seaweed

Some seaweeds grow on rocky coasts. Other, deep-water, seaweeds are often washed ashore.

Sea lace

Eel grass

Sea grass. Grows in masses on estuary banks and sheltered coasts. 1m (3¼ft)

WHEN.............................

WHERE...........................

Sea lace

Very long, thin cords wave about in underwater currents. Lives in shallow water. Up to 6m (19¾ft)

WHEN.............................

WHERE...........................

Eel grass

Channel wrack

channel wrack

Sides curve together to form grooves. Look for it on the upper shore. 10cm (4in)

WHEN.............................

WHERE...........................

Bladder wrack

sea lettuce

Found on all types of shore. Gets darker with age. 20cm (8in)

WHEN........................

WHERE...........................

Sea lettuce

Bladder wrack

Pairs of bladders (air pockets) keep it upright in the water. Root-like holdfast anchors it to rocks and sea bed. 60cm (24in)

WHEN.............................

WHERE...........................

Trees

Here are some of the words used to describe parts of a tree:

Crown

Leaf

Vein

Lobe

Fruit

Bark

Broadleaved trees have wide leaves.

Cone (fruit)

Needles

Scale

Bract

Bark

Conifer trees have thin needles.

The stickers for this section are sticker numbers 46 to 78. There are two stickers for each type of tree. You'll find all the stickers at the back of the book.

Pines

Pine trees are evergreen conifers. This means they don't lose all their leaves at once in winter, and their fruits are woody cones. They have thin, needle-like leaves.

Shore pine

Tall, fast-growing trees. Clusters of small cones. Pairs of yellow-green needles on twisted shoots. Scaly bark. Sticky, bullet-shaped buds. 23m (75ft)

WHEN.............................

WHERE............................

Shore pine

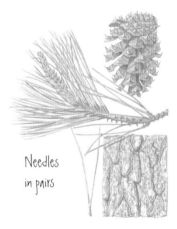

Needles in pairs

Scots pine

Long, bare trunk, red near the top

Pointed, green cones turn brown in second year

Scots pine

Short, blue-green paired needles. Small, pointed buds. Bark red at top; grey below. Young trees pointed in shape, flat-topped later. 35m (115ft)

WHEN.............................

WHERE............................

Corsican pine

Tall, fast-growing trees. Branches at regular intervals. Long, dark green, paired needles. Onion-shaped buds. Large, lop-sided brown cones. Blackish bark. 36m (118ft)

WHEN.............................

WHERE............................

Corsican pine

Cones take two years to ripen

Firs

Firs are evergreen conifers that bear cones and individual needles.

European silver fir

Common in central Europe. Tall and narrow. Flat needles (green above, silvery below) drop to leave flat, round scars on twigs. Ripe cones shed their scales. 40m (131ft)

WHEN.............................

WHERE............................

Tall, upright cones

European silver fir

Noble fir

Level branches. Dense, silver-blue needles curve upwards. Shaggy cones have down-turned bracts. Scales of cones fall off, leaving tall spikes. 37m (121ft)

WHEN.............................

WHERE............................

Noble fir

Cones grow up to 20cm (8in) long

Douglas fir

Soft needles. Long, pointed copper-brown buds. Light brown hanging cones. Old trees have thick, corky bark. 40m (131ft)

WHEN.............................

WHERE............................

Douglas fir

Cones have three-pointed bracts

cedars and larches

Cedars and larches are conifers, but not all are evergreen. Most have single needles on new shoots, and bunches of needles on old shoots.

Cone with sunken top

Atlas cedar

Large, spreading tree from the Atlas mountains of Morocco. Often in parks and gardens. Branches rise upwards. Large, upright, barrel-shaped cones with sunken tops. 25m (82ft)

WHEN.............................

WHERE.............................

Atlas cedar

Blue-green leaves in common garden variety; dark green in wild

cedar of Lebanon

Similar to Atlas cedars, but cones have rounded tops. Level branches with masses of dense foliage, giving the impression of flat "tables" of leaves. 30m (98ft)

WHEN.............................

WHERE.............................

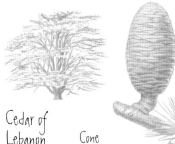

Cedar of Lebanon

Cone covered with sticky resin

Deodar cedar

Pointed crown. Soft, pale green leaves. Top shoots and branches droop. Large, barrel-shaped cones with slightly sunken tops. 23m (76ft)

WHEN.............................

WHERE.............................

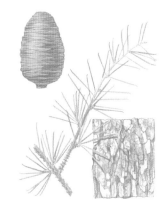

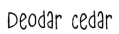

Deodar cedar

European larch

Deciduous. Bunches of soft, light green needles turn yellow and fall, leaving small knobs on twigs. Small yellow and larger reddish cones appear in early spring. Ripe cones are brown and egg-shaped and their scales lie flat. 38m (125ft)

WHEN............................

WHERE...........................

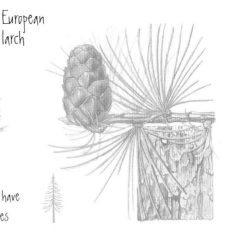

European larch

European larches have fine, light branches

Japanese larch

Japanese larches have stout branches

Japanese larch

Deciduous. Bunches of blue-green needles fall in winter, leaving orange twigs. Pinkish-green cones ripen to brown. Cone scales curl backwards like rose petals. 35m (115ft)

WHEN............................

WHERE...........................

Ripe cone

Japanese red cedar

Tall and narrow. Cone-shaped, evergreen crown. Reddish-brown, peeling bark. Long, bright green, spiky scale-like needles curve away from the twig. Green, spiky cones turn brown when ripe. 30m (98ft)

WHEN............................

WHERE...........................

Japanese red cedar

Reddish-brown peeling bark

oaks

Oaks are broadleaved trees with large leaves. Many are deciduous, which means they lose their leaves in winter. They have fruits called acorns.

Sessile oak

Narrow crown. Thick, dark green, long-stalked leaves, tapering to the base. Acorns set close to twigs. 21m (69ft)

WHEN............................

WHERE...........................

Sessile oak

Acorns more rounded than English oak

English oak

Broad crown. Acorns on long stalks. Leaves on short stalks, with ear-like lobes at the base. 23m (75ft)

WHEN............................

WHERE...........................

English oak

Broad, short trunk

Red oak

Large leaves with bristly tipped lobes turn reddish-brown in autumn. Smooth, silvery bark. Squat acorns in shallow cups ripen in second year. 20m (66ft)

WHEN............................

WHERE...........................

Autumn colour of leaves

Red oak

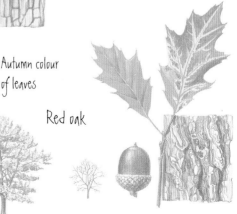

Poplars

Poplars are broadleaved, deciduous trees with simple (undivided) leaves. Some bear hanging spikes of flowers called catkins.

Lombardy poplar

Tall and narrow. Furrowed bark. Branches grow upwards. Grows along roadsides in parts of Europe. 28m (92ft)

WHEN.............................

WHERE...........................

Leaves vary slightly in shape

Lombardy poplar

Aspen

Smaller than other poplars. Often found in woods. Grey bark with large pores. Rounded, wavy-edged, deep green leaves, paler underneath. Catkins purplish-grey and fluffy on some trees; white or green and woolly on others. 20m (66ft)

WHEN.............................

WHERE...........................

Leaf stalks long and flattened

Aspen

Underside of leaf paler

Western balsam poplar

Tall and fast-growing. Long, purplish catkins. White, fluffy seeds. Large, strawberry-shaped leaves paler underneath. 35m (115ft)

WHEN.............................

WHERE...........................

Western balsam poplar

Willows

Willows are in the same family as poplars. They have catkins and simple, lobeless leaves.

Catkins known as pussy willow

Goat willow

Small and bushy. Broad, rounded, rough grey-green leaves. Silvery-grey, upright catkins develop in late winter. Grows on damp waste ground. 7m (23ft)

WHEN.............................

WHERE.............................

Goat willow

White willow

Catkins on female trees are white; male trees have yellow catkins

White willow

Grows by streams and rivers. Long, narrow, finely toothed leaves, white underneath. Slender, bendy twigs. 20m (66ft)

WHEN.............................

WHERE.............................

Crack willow

Very common willow. Grows near water. Often has branches cut back to trunk. Very long, narrow leaves, bright green above, grey-green below. Twigs easy to snap. 15m (49ft)

WHEN.............................

WHERE.............................

Very long, narrow leaves and catkins

Crack willow

22

Fruit trees

common pear

In woods and hedgerows. Big, white flowers in April. Pears sweet when ripe. Small, dark green leaves with finely toothed edges, long stalks. 15m (49ft)

WHEN.............................

WHERE............................

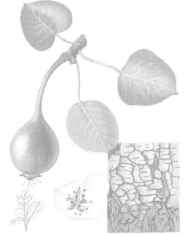

Common pear

Green pears turn golden when ripe

Wild cherry

Red cherries eaten by birds

Wild cherry

Blossom of white flowers in April. Large, dull green, oval leaves turn red in autumn. Reddish-brown bark peels in ribbons. Bitter-sweet cherries in mid-summer eaten by birds, but not usually by people. 15m (49ft)

WHEN.............................

WHERE............................

crab apple

Small, bushy trees found in hedgerows. Small, rounded leaves with toothed edges. Pinkish-white flowers in May. Small, reddish-green speckled apples too sour to eat raw, but used in cooking. 10m (33ft)

WHEN.............................

WHERE............................

Crab apple

Sour-tasting apple

More simple-leaved trees

These broadleaved trees have wide, flat leaves with wavy or toothed edges.

Southern beech

Triangular crown. Slender, oval leaves, with finely toothed edges and many obvious veins. Deep green, prickly fruit. Silver-grey bark. 20m (66ft)

WHEN..............................

WHERE.............................

Southern beech

common beech

In woods or parks. Spreading crown. Wavy-edged, oval leaves turn copper-brown in autumn. Smooth grey bark. Pointed nuts in hairy husks. 25m (82ft)

WHEN..............................

WHERE.............................

Common beech

Fruits hang from a leafy wing

common lime

Broad crown. Heart-shaped leaves with toothed edges. Yellow-green, scented flowers in July. Small, round, hard, grey-green fruits. 25m (82ft)

WHEN..............................

WHERE.............................

Common lime

Silver birch

Slender, drooping branches. Silvery, peeling bark. Small "triangular" leaves. Long spikes of tiny flowers ("catkins") in winter. 15m (49ft)

WHEN.............................

WHERE.............................

Double-toothed edges

Silver birch

Leaf edges are double-toothed

English elm

English elm

Tall. Narrow, often uneven crown. Rough, oval leaves. Red flowers in clusters. Fruit winged, see-through, turning brown when ripe. 30m (98ft)

WHEN.............................

WHERE.............................

Sweet chestnut

Sweet chestnut

Large. Tall crown. Bark may be spiral-furrowed. Long, narrow leaves with saw-toothed edges. Clusters of edible brown chestnuts in prickly green cases. 25m (82ft)

WHEN.............................

WHERE.............................

Clusters of 2–3 fruits containing nuts

compound leaves

All these broadleaved trees have compound leaves, which are made up of smaller leaflets.

Seed clusters stay on tree into winter

common ash

Woods, hedges and open hillsides. Leaves with 9 to 13 leaflets appear in late spring, after purplish flowers. Black buds. Pale grey bark. 25m (82ft)

WHEN..............................

WHERE..............................

Common ash

Flowers grow in fluffy clusters

Fruit

Manna ash

manna ash

Smooth, dark grey bark. Leaves have between five and nine stalked leaflets. Clusters of white flowers in May. Seen in towns. 20m (66ft)

WHEN..............................

WHERE..............................

Rowan flower (from a cluster)

Rowan

Small. Often found alone on mountainsides, also in towns. Toothed leaves. Clusters of creamy-white flowers in May. Red berries in August. 7m (23ft)

WHEN..............................

WHERE..............................

Rowan

Birds

Here are some of the words used to describe parts of a bird:

If the male and female don't look the same, you'll see these signs:

♀ means the picture shows a female

♂ means the picture shows a male

Crown

♀

Beak or bill

Back

♂

Breast

Rump

Belly

Wing

Tail

The stickers for this section are sticker numbers 79 to 143. You'll find all the stickers at the back of the book.

Seabirds

Gannet

Gannet

Adults white with creamy-yellow head and black wingtips. Live mostly at sea and plunge into the water to catch fish. 92cm (36¼in)

WHEN..............................

WHERE...........................

Razorbill

Black with a white breast. Large bill flat on either side. Groups nest on cliffs and spend winter out at sea. 41cm (16in)

WHEN...........................

WHERE......................

Neck and throat white in winter

Razorbill (summer)

Guillemot

Say "gilli-mot". Dark brown with white breast. Similar to razorbill, but has thinner, more pointed beak. 42cm (16½in)

WHEN..........................

WHERE....................

Neck and throat white in winter

Guillemot (summer)

Puffin

Black with white face and breast. Stripy bill and red legs in summer. Nests in holes in cliffs on rocky islands. 30cm (12in)

WHEN........................

WHERE....................

Puffin (summer)

Fulmar

Greyish-white seabird with fat bill. Nests on cliffs. Often flies close to the waves. 47cm (18½in)

WHEN............................

WHERE...........................

Fulmar

Shag
(male)

Black-headed
gull (summer)

Black-headed
gull (winter)

Shag

During breeding season, male grows crest, and feathers take on a green sheen. 76cm (30in)

WHEN.............................

WHERE...........................

Black-headed gull

Common inland. Small white gull with grey wings. Red legs and bill. Dark brown face in summer. 37cm (14½in)

WHEN.............................

WHERE...........................

common gull

Common gull

Grey and white. Yellow bill and legs. Black and white wingtips. Seen inland in winter. 41cm (16in)

WHEN.............................

WHERE....................

Herring gull

Kittiwake

Spends most time out at sea, where it can be seen following ships. Its nest is made of green seaweed, and stuck to the cliff with mud and droppings. 45cm (17¾in)

WHEN.............................

WHERE..........................

Kittiwake

Herring gull

Seaside gull with light grey back and black and white wingtips. Yellow bill with red spot. Pink legs. May nest on buildings. 56cm (22in)

WHEN.............................

WHERE...........................

Waterbirds

Wigeon

Eider

♂ ♀ Eider

Found on rocky seashores. Male black and white with lime-green ear patch. Female brown with narrow stripes. Dives for shellfish. 58cm (23in)

WHEN..............................

WHERE..........................

Wigeon

Sometimes grazes in fields, especially near the sea. Male grey body, black tail and reddish-brown head with yellow stripe. Female brown. 46cm (18in)

WHEN..............................

WHERE..........................

Mallard

Lakes and ponds. Male light grey and brown, with glossy, dark green head, yellow bill. Female streaky brown. 58cm (23in)

WHEN..............................

WHERE..........................

♂ ♀

Mallard

Canada goose

Shoveler

Easy to identify because of its long, wide bill. Male has brilliant white breast and glossy green head. Female streaky brown. 51cm (20in)

WHEN..............................

WHERE..........................

♀ Shoveler

♂

Canada goose

Large, noisy goose common in parks. Brownish-grey body. Black neck and head with white mark on chin. 95cm (37½in)

WHEN..............................

WHERE..........................

Mute
swan

Mute swan

Very common. Often seen on rivers and ponds. Large and white, with long, slender neck. Bill orange and black. Young are grey. 152cm (60in)

WHEN.............................

WHERE...........................

coot

Black all over apart from white bill and forehead. Very big feet with webbed pads. Found on large lakes. 38cm (15in)

WHEN.............................

WHERE...........................

Greylag goose

Greylag goose

Large goose sometimes found in parks, but also countryside. Brownish-grey with some white underneath. Orange bill. 82cm (32¼in)

WHEN.............................

WHERE...........................

Coot

Grey heron

Seen by rivers and lakes. Grey and white with long neck and legs. Black plumes on back of head. Eats fish and other animals. 92cm (36¼in)

WHEN.............................

WHERE...........................

Grey
heron

Moorhen

Seen near ponds and rivers. Small black bird with white markings on sides and under tail. Red and yellow bill. 33cm (13in)

WHEN.............................

WHERE...........................

Moorhen

Waders

Curlew

Curlew

Biggest wader in Britain. Streaked pale brown body. Very long, downward-curving bill. Its name comes from the sound of its long, bubbling call. 48–64cm (19–25¼in)

WHEN.............................

WHERE...........................

Knot (winter)

Knot

Often seen in huge flocks. Plump, stocky body. Winter feathers patterned dark grey on top and light grey underneath. Reddish-brown in summer. 25cm (10in)

WHEN.............................

WHERE...........................

Oystercatcher

Seen at seaside and sometimes inland. Black backs and white undersides. Pink legs. Bills are bright orange-red. 43cm (17in)

WHEN.............................

WHERE...........................

Turnstone (summer)

Turnstone

Feeds on rocky beaches by turning over stones and seaweed. Hard to see against pebbles. White underside. Back is grey in winter, reddish-brown in summer. White markings on head. 23cm (9in)

WHEN.............................

WHERE...........................

Turnstone (winter)

Ruff

Male has large plume, or ruff, of feathers around head in summer (but not in winter) which varies in colour. 23–29cm (9–11½in)

WHEN.............................

WHERE...........................

Ruff (summer)

Oystercatcher

Ruff (winter)

Ringed plover

Brown back. White belly. Black and white head. Dark band across breast on adults. Found on sandy and shingle beaches. 19cm (7½in)

WHEN...........................

WHERE.........................

Juvenile (young) bird

Ringed plover (summer)

Sanderling

Seen running on sandy beaches, catching small creatures washed up by the tide. White belly and speckled grey back in winter. Looks browner in summer. 20cm (8in)

WHEN...........................

WHERE.........................

Common sandpiper

common sandpiper

Wags tail and bobs up and down. Brown with white underside. Shortish legs and longish bill. 20cm (8in)

WHEN...........................

WHERE.........................

Sanderling (winter)

Dunlin

Small wader with brown or grey back. Black belly in summer. Seen at the seaside, and sometimes on moors in spring. 19cm (7½in)

WHEN...........................

WHERE.........................

Dunlin (winter)

Dunlin (summer)

Snipe

Snipe

Lives in marshy areas and bogs. Zigzag flight when disturbed. Speckled brown body with brown and white feathers on back. Very long beak. 27cm (10¾in)

WHEN...........................

WHERE.........................

OWLS

Little owl

Small and flat-headed. Often seen perched in daylight. Likes open country with old trees. Nests in holes. Bobs head up and down when curious. 22cm (8¾in)

WHEN...............................

WHERE..............................

Little owl

Barn owl

Breast feathers speckled white; back feathers golden-brown. Large, white, heart-shaped face. Long, screeching call. May hunt along roadside verges. 34cm (13½in)

WHEN...............................

WHERE..............................

Barn owl

Tawny owl

In woods. Speckled light and dark brown. Plump-looking, with large, round head. Big, black eyes. Calls "tu-wit" and "tu-woo". 38cm (15in)

WHEN...............................

WHERE..............................

Tawny owl

CROWS

Carrion crow and hooded crow

Hooded crow has pale grey body with black wings and head. Carrion crow all black. Both have large bill. 47cm (18½in)

WHEN...............................

WHERE..............................

Carrion crow

Hooded crow

Magpie

Magpie

Common in countryside and some towns. Black and white. Long tail. Eats eggs of other birds in spring. 46cm (18in)

WHEN...............................

WHERE..............................

Wagtails

Grey wagtail

Pied wagtail and white wagtail

Pied wagtails common in Britain; white wagtails more often seen in Europe. Tail wags up and down. 18cm (7in)

WHEN............................

WHERE..........................

Pied wagtail

White wagtail

Grey wagtail

Grey back with yellow feathers on breast and underside. Male has black patch under chin. 18cm (7in)

WHEN............................

WHERE..........................

Birds of prey

Buzzard

Golden eagle

Brown with golden neck feathers. Short, powerful beak and strong feet. Long, broad wings. Hunts animals and birds. 83cm (32¾in)

WHEN............................

WHERE..........................

Golden eagle

Buzzard

Glides on broad, rounded wings which show pale patches in flight. Also hovers. Cat-like mewing call. 54cm (21¼in)

WHEN............................

WHERE..........................

Sparrowhawk

Yellow feet. Male bluish-grey back and wings, with barred underside. Grey tail has four or five dark bars. Female larger and browner. Male: 30cm (12in) Female: 38cm (15in)

WHEN............................

WHERE..........................

Sparrowhawk

Woodpeckers

Lesser spotted woodpecker

Striped black and white, with short tail. Male has bright red crown. Rare in Britain. 14cm (5½in)

WHEN.............................

WHERE.............................

♂

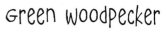

Lesser spotted woodpecker

Green woodpecker

Fairly common in woods and parks. Green wings and back. Red "cap". Call sounds like loud laugh. 32cm (12½in)

WHEN.............................

WHERE.............................

Green woodpecker

Great spotted woodpecker

♂

Great spotted woodpecker

Heard drumming on trees in spring. Black and white body. Red under tail. Male has red patch on back of head. 23cm (9in)

WHEN.............................

WHERE.............................

Pigeons and doves

Rock dove

Woodpigeon

Lives in woods, farmland and sometimes towns, often in large flocks. Grey with pinkish-brown breast. White patches on neck. 41cm (16in)

WHEN.............................

WHERE.............................

Woodpigeon

Rock dove

Grey, except for a slightly pink breast and dark, stripy markings on wings. Pink legs. Tame rock doves in towns can be many different colours. 33cm (13in)

WHEN.............................

WHERE.............................

Thrushes and starlings

Blackbird ♀

♂

Blackbird

Often in parks and gardens. Male black with bright yellow bill. Female dark brown with duller bill. 25cm (10in)

WHEN.............................

WHERE...........................

Juvenile (young) starling

Adult starling (winter)

Starling

Black-brown with glossy, green and purple sheen, and white speckles in winter. Often gathers in large flocks. 22cm (8¾in)

WHEN.............................

WHERE...........................

Fieldfare

Fieldfare

Often seen feeding on berries in autumn. Has grey head, reddish-brown back and wings, and speckled white and brown breast. 25.5cm (10in)

WHEN.............................

WHERE...........................

Song thrush

Song thrush

Often seen near trees or bushes. Well-known for breaking open snail shells by smashing them against stones. 23cm (9in)

WHEN.............................

WHERE...........................

Redwing

Redwing

In winter, usually seen eating berries or worms. Brown, with speckled breast. White eye-stripe. Reddish patch under each wing. 21cm (8¼in)

WHEN.............................

WHERE...........................

Tits and nuthatches

Long-tailed tit

Seen in hedgerows and the edges of woods, often in groups. Very long tail. Small, dumpy body. White breast. Black stripe above eye. 11cm (4¼in)

WHEN..............................

WHERE...........................

Long-tailed tit

Great tit

Blue tit

Great tit

Largest tit in the UK. Black head with white cheeks. Yellow breast with black stripe down centre. Dark bluish-grey wings and tail. 14cm (5½in)

WHEN............................

WHERE...........................

Nuthatch

Blue tit

Common in woods and gardens. Bright yellow breast. Blue feathers on wings and crown. White face, with black eye-stripe. 11cm (4¼in)

WHEN.............................

WHERE...........................

Coal tit

coal tit

Creamy-white breast. Grey wings with two pale stripes. Black head, with white patches on back and sides. 11cm (4¼in)

WHEN............................

WHERE...........................

Nuthatch

Greyish-blue wings and pale brown breast. Short tail and pointed beak. Thick, black eye-stripe. 14cm (5½in)

WHEN............................

WHERE............................

other birds

Swift

Seen in small groups in summer. Fast, skilful flier, able to sleep in the air. Dark brown, with short neck and short, forked tail. Wings very long and pointed. 17cm (6¾in)

WHEN...............................

WHERE...............................

Swift

Robin

Robin

Very common in woods and gardens. Orangey-red breast, and brown back and wings. 14cm (5½in)

WHEN...............................

WHERE...............................

House martin

Small and dark blue. Large, white patch across rump. Snow-white underneath. Short, forked tail. Catches insects in flight. 13cm (5in)

WHEN...............................

WHERE...............................

House martin

Swallow

Swallow

Very long, forked tail. Blue-black back with red markings on face. White underneath. 19cm (7½in)

WHEN...............................

WHERE...............................

Kingfisher

Brilliantly coloured. Lives near lakes and rivers. Bright blue-green wings and orange breast. Patches of white on neck. Long bill. 17cm (6¾in)

WHEN...............................

WHERE...............................

Kingfisher

other birds

cuckoo

"Cuckoo" song heard in countryside in summer. Grey, with barred breast and long tail. Lays eggs in other birds' nests. 30cm (12in)

WHEN.........................

WHERE.........................

Dipper

Cuckoo

Dipper

Lives near fast-flowing streams. Dives under water for food. Brown and black, with white breast and reddish-brown underside. 18cm (7in)

WHEN.........................

WHERE.........................

Wren

Wren

Common. Loud song. Short, round body, short wings and tail. Pointed beak. Feathers speckled brown. 9.5cm (3¾in)

WHEN.........................

WHERE.........................

Goldcrest

House sparrow

Seen near houses, though not as often as they once were. Black and brown with paler underside. Male has black face and throat. 17cm (6¾in)

WHEN.........................

WHERE.........................

♀

♂

House sparrow

Goldcrest

Smallest bird in Europe. Round body and short neck. Greenish-grey feathers, with white stripes on wings. Bright yellow stripe on crown. 9cm (3½in)

WHEN.........................

WHERE.........................

Insects

Here are some of the words used to describe parts of insects:

Giant cranefly

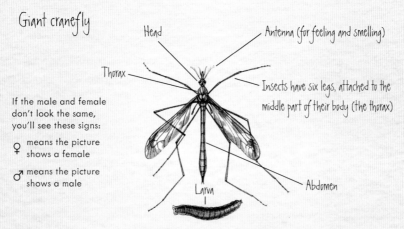

Head

Antenna (for feeling and smelling)

Thorax

Insects have six legs, attached to the middle part of their body (the thorax)

If the male and female don't look the same, you'll see these signs:

♀ means the picture shows a female

♂ means the picture shows a male

Abdomen

Larva

Many insects have young called larvae (singular: larva), that look different from the adults. Butterfly and moth larvae are called caterpillars. Other insects have young called nymphs that look like small, wingless adults.

How insects are measured:

Moths and butterflies: wingspan

Other insects: body length, not including feelers

The stickers for this section are sticker numbers 144 to 200. You'll find all the stickers at the back of the book.

Butterflies

Wall brown

Brown, with spots that look like eyes on front and back wings. Often in dry, open spaces. 44–46mm (about 1¾in)

WHEN.............................

WHERE.............................

Wall brown

Brown argus

Brown wings with orange marks near edges. Males are said to smell of chocolate when trying to attract females. 28–30mm (about 1in)

WHEN.............................

WHERE.............................

Brown argus

Clouded yellow

Pale orange wings with dark edges. Flies to Britain from southern Europe in spring. 58–62mm (2¼–2½in)

WHEN.............................

WHERE.............................

Purple hairstreak

Purple hairstreak

Flies around oak trees. Males, purplish wings with black borders; females, black wings with purple streaks on front wings. 36–39mm (about 1½in)

WHEN.............................

WHERE.............................

Marbled white

Marbled white

Marbled black and white wings. Found all over Europe; common in southern England. 53–58mm (2–2¼in)

WHEN.............................

WHERE.............................

Clouded yellow

Brimstone

Large. Male, yellow; female, greenish white. Not found in Scotland, but common in the rest of Britain. 58–62mm (2¼–2½in)

WHEN.............................

WHERE............................

♂
Brimstone

Small tortoiseshell

Common throughout the UK. Brightly patterned wings with blue half-moons along edges. 50–56mm (2–2¼in)

WHEN.............................

WHERE............................

Small
tortoiseshell

Pearl-bordered fritillary

Black markings on orange-brown wings. Pearly spots underneath. All over Britain. 42–46mm (1½–1¾in)

WHEN.............................

WHERE............................

Peacock

Peacock

Adults hibernate in winter. Large, brightly coloured wings with eye-like markings. 62–68mm (2½–2¾in)

WHEN.............................

WHERE............................

♀
Small white

Small white

Common white butterfly. Flits around gardens, especially near cabbages. 48–50mm (1¾–2in)

WHEN.............................

WHERE............................

Pearl-bordered
fritillary

Moths

Many moths fly after sunset and are attracted to lights, but the moths you're most likely to see often fly during the day.

Garden tiger

Large yellow underwing

Common. Flies into houses at night. Yellow back wings with black border. Caterpillar (called cutworm) eats grasses and other small plants. 45–60mm (1¾–2¼in)

Large yellow underwing

WHEN.............................

WHERE...........................

Cutworm

Garden tiger

Orange back wings with black spots. Front wings are mottled brown and cream. Hairy caterpillars. 60–70mm (2¼–2¾in)

WHEN.............................

WHERE............................

Silver Y

Silver Y

Brown. White markings on front wings shaped like letter "Y". Seen in spring and summer. Often flies in daytime. 40mm (1½in)

WHEN.............................

WHERE............................

Cinnabar

Hummingbird hawk-moth

Seen hovering over flowers, beating wings rapidly, like a hummingbird. Brown front wings. Orange back wings. Flies during day. 45mm (1¾in)

Hummingbird hawk-moth

WHEN.............................

WHERE...........................

cinnabar

Flies short distances by day. Back wings are red. Caterpillar is yellow and black, and feeds on ragwort. 40–45mm (1½–1¾in)

WHEN.............................

WHERE............................

Bees, wasps and ants

All the insects on this page live in big groups called colonies, led by a large female called a queen.

Buff-tailed bumblebee

Common wasp

Often lives inside a papery nest underground. Slimmer and less fuzzy than a bee. Stings to kill prey. 15–20mm (½–¾in)

WHEN............................

WHERE............................

Common wasp

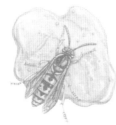

Buff-tailed bumblebee

Big, furry, black and yellow body with pale tip. Queen makes nest in hole in the ground. 22mm (¾in)

WHEN............................

WHERE............................

Honey bee

Golden brown body with black stripes. Colonies make honey in their hive. 12–17mm (½–¾in)

WHEN............................

WHERE............................

Hornet

Hornet

Very large wasp. Brown and yellow markings on rear part. 22–30mm (¾–1in)

WHEN............................

WHERE............................

Every honey bee has a job:

One female, the queen, lays the eggs.

Black ant

Male has wings, and dies after flying and mating. Queen only female with wings. Loses them after mating, then starts a colony. 3–9mm (1/8–¼in)

WHEN............................

WHERE............................

Black ants

Winged males

Wingless female worker

Males, called drones, mate with the queen.

Females, called workers, do the work.

True flies and lacewings

True flies have two wings, while many other flying insects have four.

Common gnat

Giant cranefly or daddy-long-legs

Large fly seen near water. Long, spindly body. Very long legs. Larvae, called leatherjackets, eat root crops and grass roots. 30–40mm (1–1½in)

WHEN...........................

WHERE...........................

Leatherjacket

Giant cranefly

common gnat or mosquito

Common. Golden-brown. Very long, thin legs. Female sucks blood from people and animals. 6–7mm (about ¼in)

WHEN...........................

WHERE...........................

Bluebottle

Bluebottle

Blue, hairy fly that buzzes loudly as it searches for rotting meat to lay its eggs on. Male laps nectar from flowers. 9–15mm (¼–½in)

WHEN...........................

WHERE...........................

Green lacewing

Hover fly

Looks like a wasp, but doesn't sting. Many types. This one is brown, with three light stripes on side of body. 10–14mm (about ½in)

WHEN...........................

WHERE...........................

Hover fly

Green lacewing

Four wings covered with green, lace-like veins. Seen mainly around gardens and hedges. 15mm (½in)

WHEN...........................

WHERE...........................

True bugs

True bugs are insects with sharp mouth-parts which they use for sucking the juices from plants, or, in a few cases, animals.

Rose aphid

Black bean aphid or blackfly

Broad beans and thistles often house large groups of this tiny, black bug. 2–3mm (about ⅛in)

WHEN..............................

WHERE............................

Black bean aphid

Rose aphid or greenfly

Green or pink. Shaped like a bulb. Feeds on roses in spring. Produces sweet, sticky syrup called honeydew, which ants eat. 2–3mm (about ⅛in)

WHEN..............................

WHERE............................

Green shieldbug

Green shieldbug

Seen on trees such as hazel and birch. Broad, green body with light brown rear end. 12–14mm (½in)

WHEN..............................

WHERE............................

Black and red froghopper

common froghopper

Can jump 70cm (28in) into the air. Young (called nymphs) live on plant stems and make a froth called cuckoo spit, in which they hide. 6mm (¼in)

WHEN..............................

WHERE............................

Common froghopper

Black and red froghopper

Stripy. Jumps, and makes "cuckoo spit". Bold colours warn animals it tastes nasty. 9–10mm (about ¼in)

WHEN..............................

WHERE............................

Beetles

There are more types of beetle than any other creature on land. Here are just a few of the kinds you might spot.

Great silver water beetle

Devil's coach horse or cocktail beetle

Seen in parks and gardens. Squirts its enemies with foul-smelling liquid from its tail. 25–30mm (about 1in)

WHEN..............................

WHERE...........................

Devil's coach horse

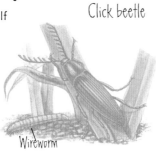

Great silver water beetle

Britain's largest water beetle. Large, black body with hairy back legs. Claws on front legs. 37–48mm (1½–1¾in)

WHEN..............................

WHERE...........................

Seven-spot ladybird

Seven-spot ladybird

Colour warns other animals it doesn't taste good. Releases foul-smelling liquid if threatened. Spends winter indoors. 6–8mm (about ¼in)

WHEN..............................

WHERE...........................

Water beetle

Click beetle or skip-jack

If it falls on its back, it flips itself into the air with a loud click. Many types: this one has branched feelers. Larvae called wireworms. 14–18mm (½–¾in)

WHEN..............................

WHERE...........................

Click beetle

Wireworm

Water beetle

In lakes and rivers. Brown or black. Lays eggs on water plants. 7–8mm (about ¼in)

WHEN..............................

WHERE...........................

Horned dung beetle or minotaur beetle

Black with broad, ribbed wing cases, and tough, thick legs. Large horns around head used for fighting each other. Found in sandy places. Eats dung. 12–18mm (½–¾in)

WHEN...............................

WHERE..........................

Horned dung beetle

Stag beetle

Stag beetle

Largest beetle in Britain. Male has purplish wing cases, black head and legs, and long, antler-like jaws. 25–75mm (1–3in)

WHEN...............................

WHERE...........................

Nut weevil

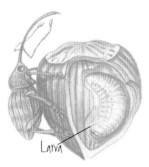

Larva

Nut weevil

Females use their long snouts to bore into hazelnuts, then lay eggs in the holes. Larvae grow inside the nuts, eating the kernels. 10mm (½in)

WHEN...............................

WHERE..........................

♀

Larva

♂

Glow-worm

Death watch beetle

Eats wood in timber buildings. Makes a ticking noise, knocking its head on walls as it tunnels through wood. Ticking was once thought to mean that someone was about to die. 7–10mm (¼– ½in)

WHEN...............................

WHERE..........................

Death watch beetle

Glow-worm

Female has long, brown body without wings or wing cases. Tail glows to attract males. Female: 20mm (¾in) Male: 15mm (½in)

WHEN...............................

WHERE..........................

Dragonflies and damselflies

Emperor dragonfly

Seen over ponds and lakes in summer. Largest dragonfly in Britain. Hunts butterflies and other flying insects. 10.5cm (4in)

WHEN.............................

WHERE.............................

Emperor dragonfly

Downy emerald

♂

Downy emerald

See-through wings. Bright green body. 68mm (2¾in)

WHEN.............................

WHERE.............................

Blue-tailed damselfly

Named because of blue tip of long abdomen. Clear wings. Rests on plants in wet areas. 35mm (1¼in)

WHEN.............................

WHERE.............................

Blue-tailed damselfly

♂

Broad-bodied chaser

Yellow markings. Males are pale blue, females are brown. 75mm (3in)

WHEN.............................

WHERE.............................

♂

Broad-bodied chaser

Ruddy darter

Golden-brown body and see-through wings. Seen around weedy ponds or ditches in marshy areas. Becoming rarer. 55mm (2in)

WHEN.............................

WHERE.............................

Ruddy darter

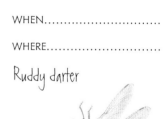

♂

Banded demoiselle

Males are blue with bright blue flashes on each wing. Females are green with see-through green wings. 60–65mm (2¼–2½in)

WHEN.............................

WHERE.............................

♂

Banded demoiselle

cockroaches and crickets

Common cockroach

common cockroach

Comes into houses for warmth. Large, black or brown and shiny. Spiny legs and long antennae. Front of thorax covers head like a helmet. 25mm (1in)

WHEN.............................

WHERE...........................

German cockroach

Despite its name, is probably from north Africa or the Middle East. Light brown body. Two dark streaks on head. Long, folded wing cases. 13mm (½in)

WHEN.............................

WHERE...........................

German cockroach

House cricket

House cricket

Found in rubbish heaps, heated buildings and greenhouses. Males "sing" a shrill song which gets louder as the temperature rises. 16mm (½in)

WHEN.............................

WHERE...........................

Mole cricket

Mole cricket

Digs using spade-shaped front feet. Thorax grows over head, looking like armour. Male has a long, whirring call. 38–42mm (about 1½in)

WHEN.............................

WHERE...........................

Field cricket

Very rare. Black body and legs, long antennae and brown wing cases. Males "sing" by rubbing wing cases together, to attract females. 20mm (¾in)

WHEN.............................

WHERE...........................

Field cricket

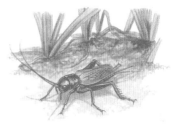

other insects

praying mantis

Long, green body, and small head.
Holds front legs together, as if praying,
while lying in wait for insects. Found
in scrub and tall grass in Southern
Europe. 60–80mm (2¼–3in)

WHEN.............................

WHERE.............................

Praying mantis

Mouthparts at
end of snout

Stick insect

stick insect

Very long, thin, green body that looks like
a stick. Lives in bushes. Small number can
be found in southwest Britain. A similar
type, called the laboratory stick insect,
often kept as a pet. Up to 90mm (3½in)

WHEN.............................

WHERE.............................

Large marsh grasshopper

Only in boggy areas. Yellow and black
abdomen, red and brown head and thorax.
Male has slow, ticking song and wings
look silvery in flight. 27–32mm (1–1¼in)

WHEN.............................

WHERE.............................

Large marsh
grasshopper

Female's pincers
are straighter

♂

Common
earwig

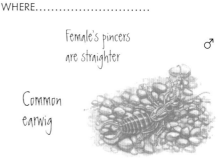

common earwig

Tiny wing cases. Abdomen has
pincers at end. Spreads and raises
pincers when threatened. Doesn't
often fly. 15mm (½in)

WHEN.............................

WHERE.............................

Animals

How the animals in this section are measured:

Hoofed mammals:
shoulder height

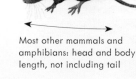

Most other mammals and
amphibians: head and body
length, not including tail

Shelled animals:
length of shell

Spiders: body length,
not including legs

Other creepy-crawlies:
body length

The stickers for this section are sticker
numbers 201 to 282. You'll find all the
stickers at the back of the book.

cattle

British Limousin

Reddish-brown cattle. Most common
breed in the UK. Bred mainly for beef.
1.4m (4½ft)

WHEN..............................

WHERE..............................

British Limousin

Bull

charolais

Heavyweight, creamy-white breed
mainly farmed for beef. Originally
from France. 1.5m (5ft)

WHEN..............................

WHERE..............................

Charolais

Bull

Holstein Friesian

Cow

Holstein Friesian

These large, black and white cows
produce more milk than any other
breed. 1.52m (5ft)

WHEN..............................

WHERE..............................

Aberdeen Angus

Bull

Aberdeen Angus

Hardy, black Scottish breed. No
horns. It is valued for the high
quality of its meat. 1.4m (4½ft)

WHEN..............................

WHERE..............................

sheep and pigs

North of England mule

This widespread sheep is a cross between a long-woolled Bluefaced Leicester and a hill breed, such as a Swaledale. 70cm (28in)

WHEN.............................

WHERE.............................

North of England mule

Scottish blackface

A tough sheep that lives on hills and moors. The most common breed in Britain. Both rams (males) and ewes (females) have horns. 70cm (28in)

WHEN.............................

WHERE.............................

Scottish blackface

Suffolk

A hornless breed with a black head and legs, and short, white wool. 77cm (30¼in)

WHEN.............................

WHERE.............................

Suffolk

Gloucester Old Spot

Spotty pig prized for its pork. Usually kept outdoors. Its ancestors used to live in orchards. 89cm (35in)

WHEN.............................

WHERE.............................

Gloucester Old Spot

Large white

Large white

This big, common, pale pink pig is bred mainly for bacon. Can have more than 14 piglets in a litter. 91cm (35¾in)

WHEN.............................

WHERE.............................

55

other mammals

Many mammals are active in the early morning, evening or at night. To spot them, you'll have to be patient, and keep very still.

Hedgehog

Hedgehog

Prickly spines. Seen at night. Hunts for slugs and worms. Rolls into a ball when scared. Fairly noisy: snuffles, snores and squeals. 25cm (9¾in)

WHEN.............................

WHERE..........................

Grey Squirrel

Acrobatic mammal that lives in trees. Often seen in parks and woods. Builds large nests, called dreys, from twigs and leaves. 27cm (10¾in)

WHEN.............................

WHERE..........................

Grey squirrel

House mouse

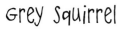

House mouse

Lives near people. Eats scraps, insects, grain and fruit. Tail as long as body. Nests in buildings. Each nest holds from 4 to 8 furless young that grow into adults in a month. 9cm (3½in)

WHEN.............................

WHERE..........................

Brown rat

Brown rat

Eats nearly anything – even soap. Lives in a large pack in buildings during winter; and in sewers, canals and river banks during summer. 26cm (10¼in)

WHEN.............................

WHERE..........................

Rabbit

Rabbit

Seen on grassy wasteland. Lives in a group in large, underground burrow network, called a warren. Wild rabbit brown-grey with pale belly and white beneath tail. 40cm (15¾in)

WHEN.............................

WHERE..........................

common Shrew

Fast and fidgety. Lives in thick grass or bushes. Eats worms and insects. Pointed, flexible snout. Tiny eyes. Sometimes nests in rubbish heaps. 7cm (2¾in)

WHEN............................

WHERE............................

Common Shrew

Mole

Pipistrelle bat

Seen at dusk. Catches flying insects. Flies in jerky fashion. Sleeps in hollow trees or dark buildings during the day. 20–25cm (8–9¾in)

WHEN............................

WHERE............................

Mole

Velvety, black body. Lives underground. Digs tunnels with strong front claws. Molehills are heaps of waste soil from these tunnels. Eats worms. 13cm (5in)

WHEN............................

WHERE............................

Badger

Pipistrelle bat

FOX

Nimble. Rust-red, with white underside. Bushy tail. Can be seen in towns and gardens. Comes out mainly at night. Scavenges food from bins. Male fox is called a dog; female is a vixen. 67cm (26½in)

WHEN............................

WHERE............................

Fox

Badger

Digs a burrow, called a sett, in woods. Spends the day underground. At night searches for wide range of food, including worms, insects, grubs, nuts and berries. Sometimes raids bins. 75cm (30in)

WHEN............................

WHERE............................

common dormouse

Lives in woods and hedges. Uses honeysuckle bark to build its hibernation and breeding nests. Nocturnal and solitary. Climbs well. Eats insects, berries, seeds, hazelnuts and chestnuts. 8cm (3in)

WHEN.............................

WHERE...........................

Weasel

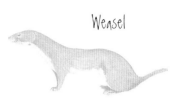

Common dormouse

Long, fluffy tail

weasel

Runs with an arched back. Hunts at night. Eats small mammals and birds. Lives in woods and farmland, and on mountains. Prefers dry areas. Not found in Ireland. 20cm (7¾in)

WHEN.............................

WHERE...........................

Fallow deer

♂

Fallow deer

Lives in herds in parks and woods. Young are born with spotted coats. Eats herbs, grass, berries, acorns and leaves. 1m (3¼ft)

WHEN.............................

WHERE...........................

Stoat

otter

Found along marshes, rivers, lakes and coastal areas, and on offshore islands. Lives on its own. Active at night. Expert swimmer. Eats fish, crabs, eels, frogs, waterfowl and rabbits. 70cm (28in)

WHEN.............................

WHERE...........................

Otter

stoat

Found in woods, on farmland and on mountains. Northern stoats, called ermines, are white in winter. Tip of tail is always black. Eats rabbits, small rodents, birds and eggs. 28cm (11in)

WHEN.............................

WHERE...........................

Sea mammals

Seals live on the seashore. Porpoises and dolphins live in the sea, but you might spot them when they come up for air.

Grey seal

Lives in small colonies on rocky shores. Rests on land at low tide and sunset, but sleeps in the sea. 2.9m (9½ft)

WHEN.............................

WHERE...........................

Grey seal

Mediterranean monk seal

Very rare. Lives on small rocky beaches on islands. 2.4m (8ft)

WHEN.............................

WHERE...........................

Mediterranean monk seal

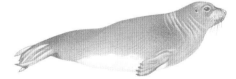

Common seal

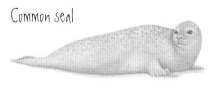

common seal

Lives in herds on sandbanks in estuaries. Fast swimmer. Can stay under water for half an hour. 1.8m (6ft)

WHEN.............................

WHERE...........................

Common porpoise

common porpoise

Small whale with blunt nose. Often swims near the coast in groups. Eats squid and fish. 1.8m (6ft)

WHEN.............................

WHERE...........................

Common dolphin

common dolphin

Fast swimmer. Lives in large groups. Very playful. Often jumps right out of the water. 2.4m (8ft)

WHEN.............................

WHERE...........................

Fishes

You might spot these fishes on the seashore, either in the sand at low tide or in rock pools.

Sand eel

Dab

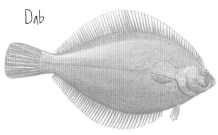

Dab

Seen in shallow water on muddy or sandy bottoms. Eyes on one side of head. Eats small crustaceans. 25cm (9¾in)

WHEN.............................

WHERE.............................

Greater pipefish

On muddy or sandy bottoms. Eats young fish and tiny crustaceans. Hides in seaweed or eel grass. 45cm (17¾in)

WHEN.............................

WHERE.............................

Greater pipefish

Sand eel

These fish live in huge groups, called schools, close to the sea bottom in shallow water. They burrow headfirst into the sand. 20cm (7¾in)

WHEN.............................

WHERE.............................

Corkwing wrasse

Starts life female but may become male later. Eats animals with shells. Lives in shallow water. 25cm (9¾in)

WHEN.............................

WHERE.............................

Corkwing wrasse (male)

Butterfish

Butterfish

Lives in cool water. Slippery. Slides between rocks. Also seen under seaweed and stones. 25cm (9¾in)

WHEN.............................

WHERE.............................

Sea scorpion

Lives in pools on the shore and among seaweed. Eats shrimps, small crabs, and other fish. 17cm (6¾in)

WHEN...............................

WHERE............................

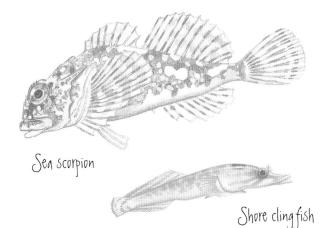

Sea scorpion

Montagu's blenny

Lives in rock pools. Eats acorn barnacles when they poke out of their shell. 8cm (3in)

WHEN...............................

WHERE............................

Montagu's blenny

Shore clingfish

Shore clingfish

Lives under rocks, clinging on with a sucker fin. Colour varies from pink to green. In the summer, pairs of clingfish guard their eggs. 6.5cm (2½in)

WHEN...............................

WHERE............................

Shanny

Lives in seaweed in pools on rocky and sandy shores. Changes skin colour from grey to brown or green to match its surroundings. Eats crustaceans. 16cm (6¼in)

WHEN...............................

WHERE............................

Shanny

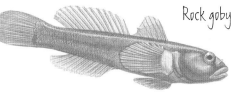

Rock goby

Rock goby

Lives on rocky shores, in pools and under stones. Eyes on top of its head, to keep a look out for predators. 12cm (4¾in)

WHEN...............................

WHERE............................

crustaceans and jellyfish

Crustaceans are creatures with shells and jointed legs.

Shore crab

Edible crab

Edible crab

Lives in deep water. Small ones seen in rock pools, or buried under sand on lower shore. Popular seafood. Up to 11.5cm (4½in)

WHEN.............................

WHERE...........................

Shore crab

Smooth, broad shell that varies from dark green to red. Very common on sandy and rocky shores. 4cm (1½in)

WHEN.............................

WHERE...........................

Squat lobster

Squat lobster

Actually a crab. Found under rocks and stones on the lower shore. Up to 6.5cm (2½in)

WHEN.............................

WHERE...........................

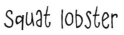

Common prawn

common hermit crab

Finds empty shells to live in. When it outgrows one shell, it looks for a larger one. Up to 10cm (4in)

WHEN.............................

WHERE...........................

Common hermit crab

common prawn

Common in shallow water, and can be found in rock pools, too. Can be told from other prawns and shrimps by the sawteeth on its snout. 6.5cm (2½in)

WHEN.............................

WHERE...........................

common shrimp

Common in sandy estuaries. Has broad, flat claws on its front legs. People catch shrimps and prawns to eat. 5cm (2in)

WHEN.............................

WHERE.............................

Common shrimp

Acorn barnacle

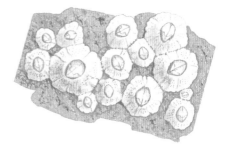

Acorn barnacle

Sticks to a rock and builds a hard shell around itself that has a diamond-shaped opening in the top. 1.5cm (½in)

WHEN.............................

WHERE.............................

Moon jellyfish

Common and harmless. Four tentacles. Transparent with purple rim, and four pale purple rings in the middle. Body 15cm (6in) wide.

WHEN.............................

WHERE.............................

Moon jelly fish

Sea gooseberry

Distant relative of jellyfish. Size of a gooseberry. Traps food in two sticky tentacles. Body 1cm (½in) wide.

WHEN.............................

WHERE.............................

Stalked jelly fish

stalked jellyfish

Harmless. Funnel-shaped body has tentacles around its rim. Attaches itself to seaweed on shore. 2.5cm (1in)

WHEN.............................

WHERE.............................

Sea gooseberry

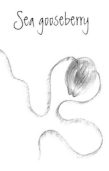

Molluscs

Molluscs are soft-bodied animals. Many have protective outer shells. Some molluscs live on the shore; others live out at sea.

Common squid

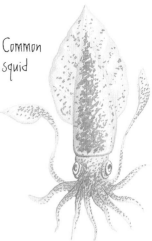

Curled octopus

Lives among rocks. Occasionally seen on extreme lower shore, when tide is far out. Colour can be yellow to reddish-brown. 20cm (7¾in)

WHEN..............................

WHERE..............................

Curled octopus

common squid

Lives in the open sea. Has an inner shell (called a pen) that can be found washed up on the beach. 60cm (23in)

WHEN..............................

WHERE..............................

Common mussel

common whelk

Whelks are gastropods, which means they have a muscular foot that clings to rocks or seaweed. They live in the sea, but empty shells are found on beaches. 8cm (3in)

WHEN..............................

WHERE..............................

Common whelk

Common limpet

common mussel

Blue or brown. Found on rocky shores and estuaries. Attaches itself to rock with thin threads. People collect this kind of mussel to eat. 7cm (2¾in)

WHEN..............................

WHERE..............................

common limpet

Limpets are gastropods (see whelk), and clamp onto rocks. They feed on seaweed and are seen on rocky shores when tide is out. 7cm (2¾in)

WHEN..............................

WHERE..............................

starfish and sea urchins

common starfish

Like most starfishes, has five arms. If one arm breaks off, a new one can grow. Uses its rows of suckers to climb up rocks. 5–10cm (2–4in)

WHEN..........................

WHERE..........................

Common starfish

Spiny starfish

spiny starfish

Has sharp spikes for defence. Lives on low shore, and in deep water. 8–12cm (3–4¾in)

WHEN..............................

WHERE..............................

Common brittle star

common brittle star

Lives under stones in rock pools. Arms break easily, so should be handled gently. 3–8cm (1–3in)

WHEN..............................

WHERE..............................

Edible sea urchin

Purple-tipped sea urchin

Lives under rocks on lower shore. Spines have purple tips. More common than edible sea urchin. 4cm (1½in)

WHEN..............................

WHERE..............................

Purple-tipped sea urchin

Edible sea urchin

Scrapes algae off rocks with teeth on the base of its body. Eaten in many countries. 15cm (6in)

WHEN..............................

WHERE..............................

Anemones and sponges

Sea anemones and sponges may look like flowers, but are actually animals. They're mostly seen on underwater rocks.

Beadlet anemone

Plumose anemone

Orange or white. Often seen just below the water's surface on pier supports. 20cm (7¾in) wide.

WHEN.............................

WHERE.............................

Plumose anemone

Beadlet anemone

Red or green with blue spots, and thin blue line around base. Lives in rock pools. 3cm (1¼in) wide.

WHEN.............................

WHERE.............................

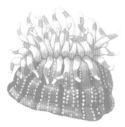

Dahlia anemone

Many different colours. Hard to spot, because body often covered with pieces of shell. 6–7cm (2¼–2¾in) wide.

WHEN.............................

WHERE.............................

Dahlia anemone

Purse sponge

Encrusting sponge

Forms crusts over rocks. Has many small openings all over its surface. 50cm (19¾in) wide.

WHEN.............................

WHERE.............................

Encrusting sponge

Purse sponge

Hangs down in groups under rocks, in pools and among seaweeds. Collapses into a purse shape when out of the water. 1–2cm (½–¾in) wide.

WHEN.............................

WHERE.............................

Worms

You can find worms in sand on the seashore or in soil. Some burrow into the ground, and others wriggle along the surface.

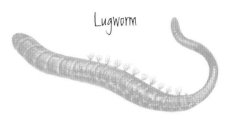
Lugworm

Green leaf worm

Green leaf worm

On rocky shores. Crawls among barnacles and under seaweed, or hides in crevices. 10cm (4in)

WHEN............................

WHERE..........................

Lugworm

Burrows in sand. Sucks in the sand, digests it, then passes it out, leaving spaghetti-like sandcasts on the surface. 15cm (6in)

WHEN............................

WHERE..........................

Earthworm

Seen above soil after rain. Pointed, brownish-red front end. Pale back end. "Saddle" in between. Eats dead plants. 10–30cm (4–11¾in)

WHEN............................

WHERE..........................

Keelworm

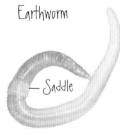
Earthworm

— Saddle

Keelworm

Lives on rocks, stones or empty shells on the seashore in a hard, white tube with a ridge along the top. Males have yellow bodies; females are violet. 3cm (1¼in)

WHEN............................

WHERE..........................

Ragworm

Digs a burrow in sand and mud, in which it spins a sticky net to catch food. Has a red line down its back. 10cm (4in)

WHEN............................

WHERE..........................

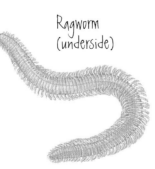
Ragworm (underside)

Amphibians and reptiles

common toad

Warty skin. Only enters water to breed. Hides by day, comes out at night. Hunts slugs, snails, worms and insects. 13cm (5in)

WHEN.............................

WHERE..........................

Common toad

Toadspawn

Common frog

Frogspawn

common frog

Smooth skin. Eats slugs, snails and insects. Lives mainly on land, but mates and lays eggs in water. 10cm (4in)

WHEN.............................

WHERE..........................

Smooth newt

♂

Tadpole

Eggs on water plants

♀

Smooth newt

Male spends spring in water. Before breeding, they grow a crest along back and tail. Female enters water to mate and lay eggs. 11cm (4¼in)

WHEN.............................

WHERE..........................

Tadpoles

Frogs and toads lay eggs, called spawn, that hatch into tadpoles. These go through a series of changes as they grow.

WHEN.............................

WHERE..........................

Long tail

Legs appear

Legs grow

Grows lungs and moves onto land

grass snake

Not poisonous. Good swimmer. Hunts frogs and toads, and swallows them alive. 120cm (47¼in)

WHEN.............................

WHERE..........................

Grass snake

creepy-crawlies

Insects have six legs, but some creepy-crawlies, for example millipedes, have many more. Others, such as slugs and snails, slither along on a single "foot".

Centipede

centipede

Long, segmented, and shiny chestnut brown body. Around 30 legs. Lives in damp, dark places. Uses front claws to poison insects and slugs. 18–30mm (¾–1¼in)

WHEN.............................

WHERE..........................

garden spider

Yellow-brown. Has a cross-shaped pattern of white spots on back. Spins sticky web to catch flying insects, and often hangs, head-down, at its centre. 7–18mm (¼–¾in)

WHEN.............................

WHERE..........................

Garden spider

snake millipede

Tube-shaped body. About 100 legs. Active at night. Feeds on rotten wood and plant roots. Coils up if disturbed. 20–30mm (¾–1¼in)

WHEN.............................

WHERE..........................

Snake millipede

garden snail

Common. Grey body. Large, yellow-brown shell with dark bands. Hides under stones in the day. Comes out at night to feed on plants. 25–35mm (1–1½in)

WHEN.............................

WHERE..........................

Garden snail

Garden slug

garden slug

Yellowish-grey with black stripes. Orange underside. Leaves yellow trail of slime. Spends day in damp, shady places. Emerges at night, or after rain. 25–30mm (1–1¼in)

WHEN.............................

WHERE..........................

Useful words

amphibian – an animal that can live both on land and in water

bank – sloping land beside a lake, river or stream

bird of prey – a bird that hunts and kills other animals for food

bud – a swelling on a stem or branch that grows into a leaf or flower

carnivore – an animal that feeds on other animals

colony – a group of the same kind of animal that live together

compound leaf – a leaf that is made up of smaller leaflets

creeping plant – a plant that grows low along the ground

estuary – a place where a large river meets the sea

fruit – part of a tree that holds its seeds

habitat – the area where a plant or animal lives

herbivore – an animal that feeds on plants

hibernation – when an animal spends the winter in a sleepy state

lobed – a type of leaf with divided parts that have rounded edges

mammal – an animal that is usually hairy, feeds its babies with milk and has a constant body temperature

marsh – an area of low-lying land that gets flooded either by a river or the sea

migration – a regular movement of animals from one place to another and back again to feed or breed

moor – an open area of land that is wet and windy

nocturnal – active at night

omnivores – animals that feed on plants and animals

predator – an animal that kills and eats other animals

prey – an animal that is hunted and killed by other animals

reptile – a scaly-skinned animal whose body temperature depends on the temperature of its surroundings

sand dune – a mound or ridge of loose sand formed by the wind

shingle – a beach made up of small pebbles that have been worn to roughly the same size by the sea

simple leaf – a leaf that is one undivided shape

species – a group of animals or plants that can reproduce together

tendril – a thin stem or leaf that helps a plant to climb

wader – a long-legged bird that lives near water and often wades in search of food

Index

This list will help you find every plant, tree and animal in the book. The first number after each entry tells you which page it's on. The second number (in brackets) is the number of its sticker(s).

Cover design: Karen Tomlins Digital imaging: Keith Furnival
This edition first published in 2011 by Usborne Publishing Ltd., Usborne House, 83-85 Saffron Hill, London, EC1N 8RT, England.
www.usborne.com Copyright © 2011– 1976 Usborne Publishing Ltd.The name Usborne and the devices are Trade Marks of Usborne Publishing Ltd.

1

2

3

4

5

6

7

8

9

10

11

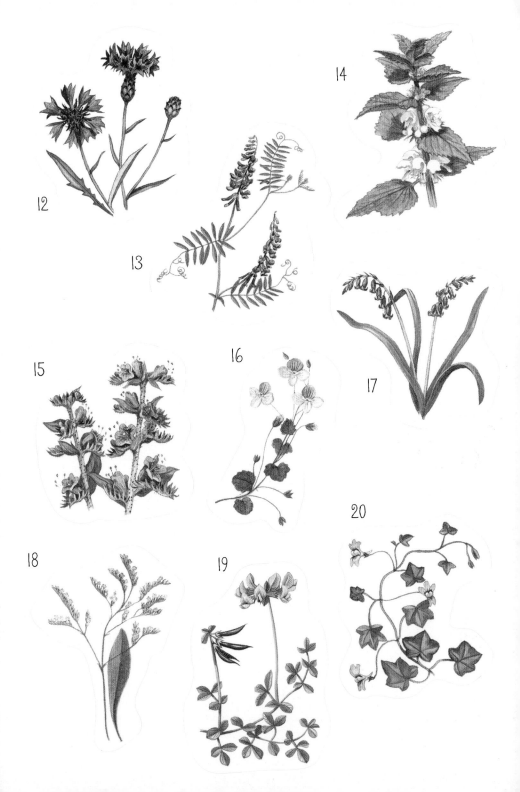

12

13

14

15

16

17

18

19

20

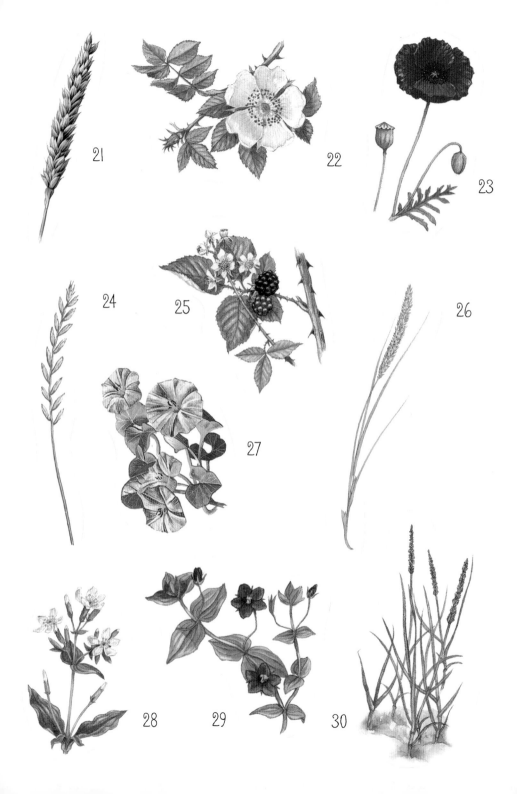

21

22

23

24

25

26

27

28

29

30

31

32

33

34

36

35

39

37

38

40

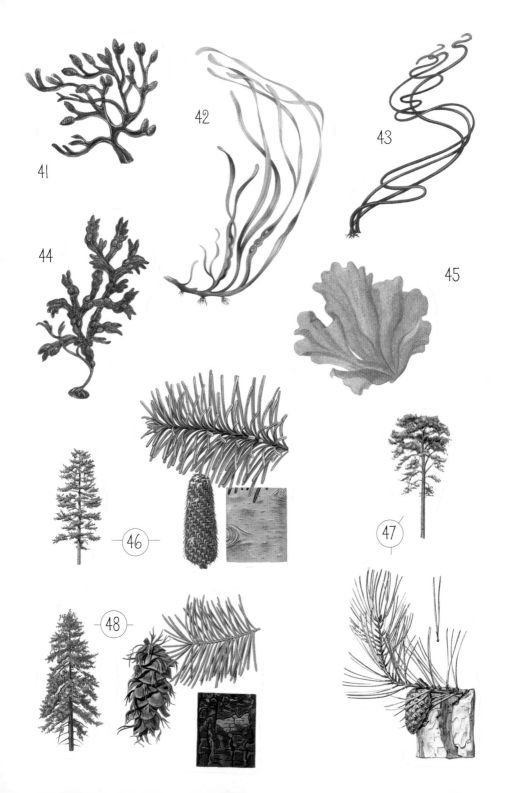

41

42

43

44

45

46

47

48

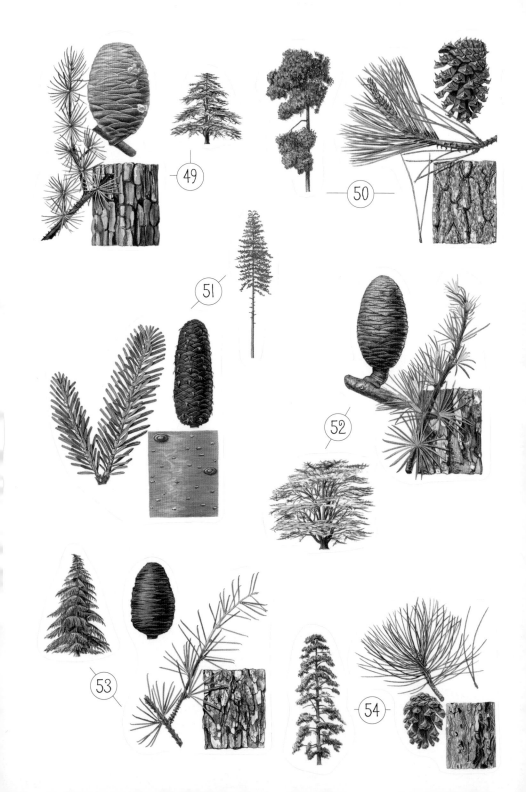

49

50

51

52

53

54

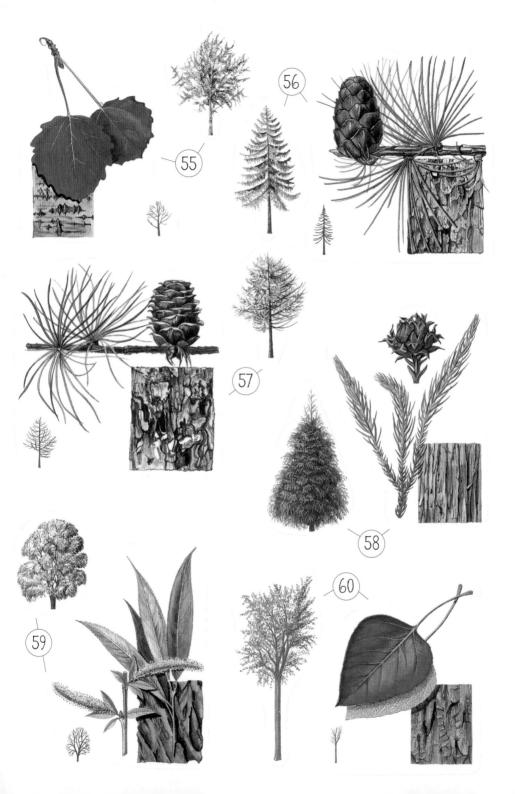

55

56

57

58

59

60

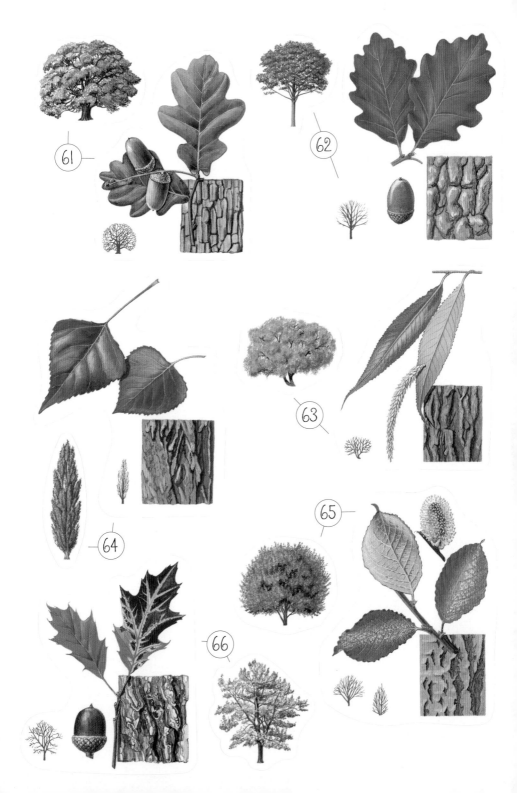

61

62

63

64

65

66

67

68

69

70

71

72

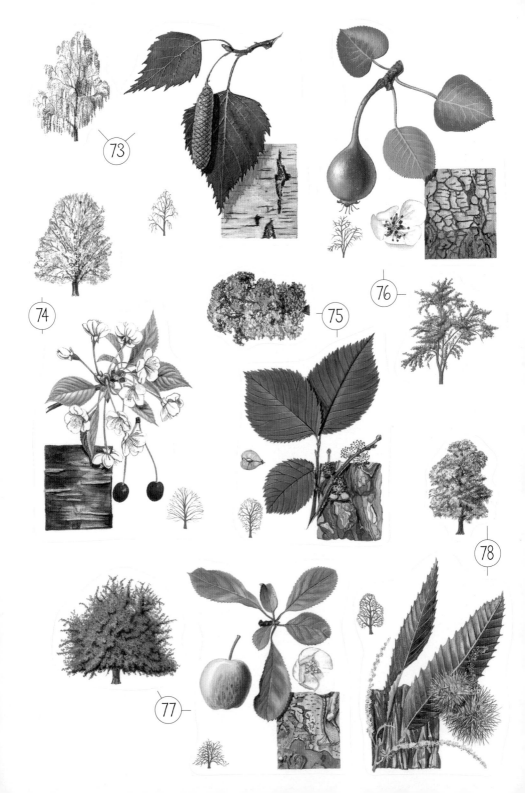

73

74

75

76

77

78

89

90

91

92

93

94

95

96

97

98

99

100

101

102

103

104

105

106

107

108

109

110

111

112

113

114

115

116

117

118

119

120

121

122

123

124

125

126

127

128

129

130

131

132

134

133

135

136

137

138

139

140

141

142

143

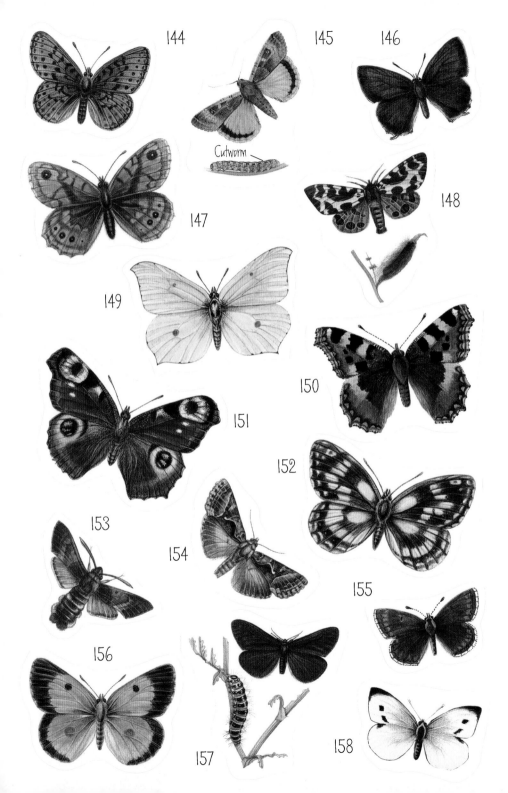

144

145

146

Cutworm

147

148

149

150

151

152

153

154

155

156

157

158

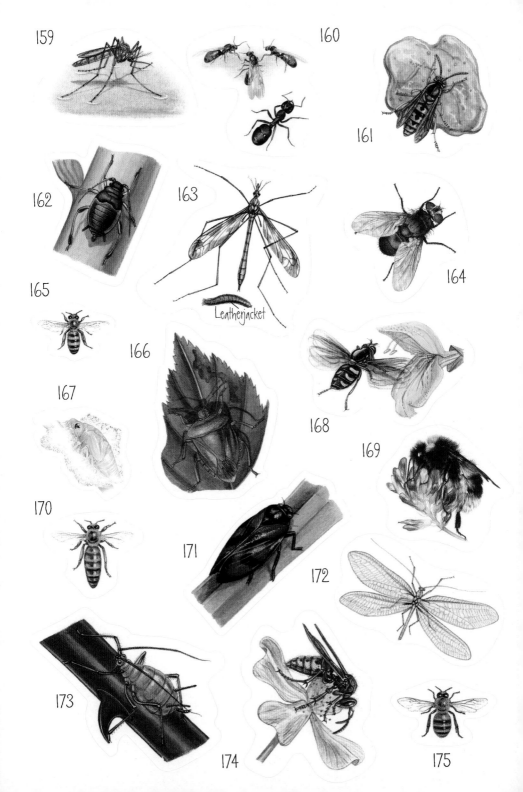

159

160

161

162

163

164

165

166

167

168

169

170

171

172

173

174

175

Leatherjacket

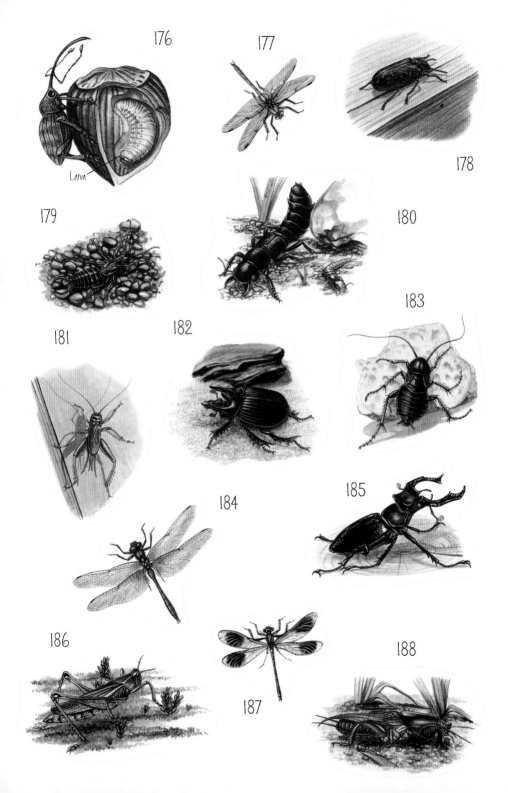

176

177

178

179

180

181

182

183

184

185

186

187

188

Larva

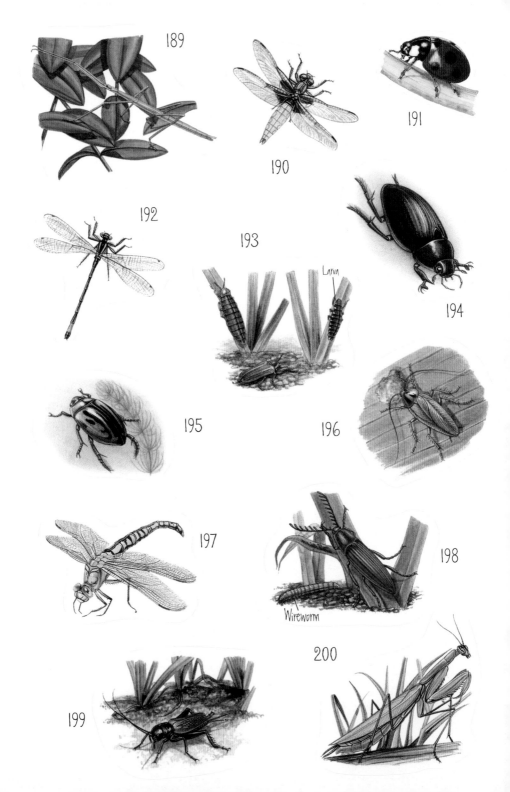

189

190

191

192

193

Larva

194

195

196

197

198

Wireworm

199

200

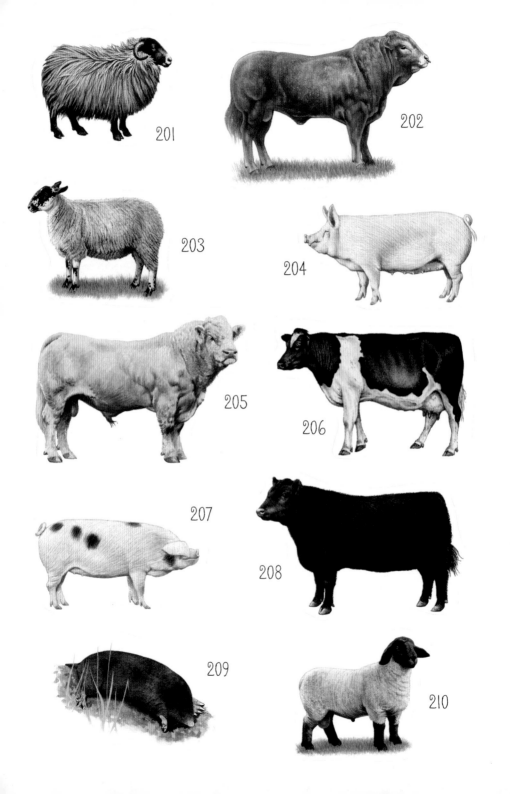

201

202

203

204

205

206

207

208

209

210

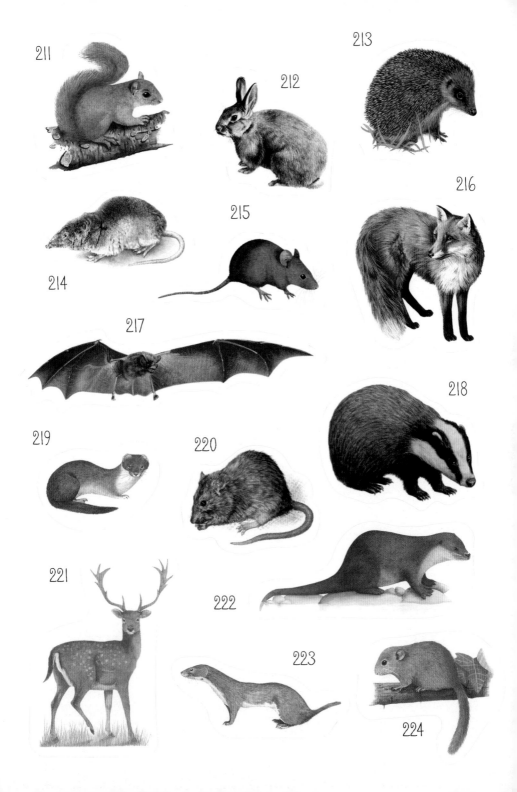

211

212

213

214

215

216

217

218

219

220

221

222

223

224

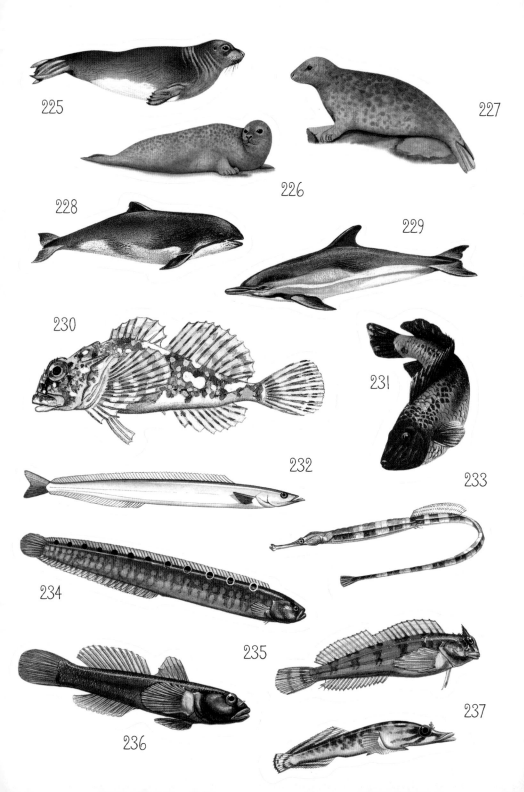

225

227

226

228

229

230

231

232

233

234

235

236

237

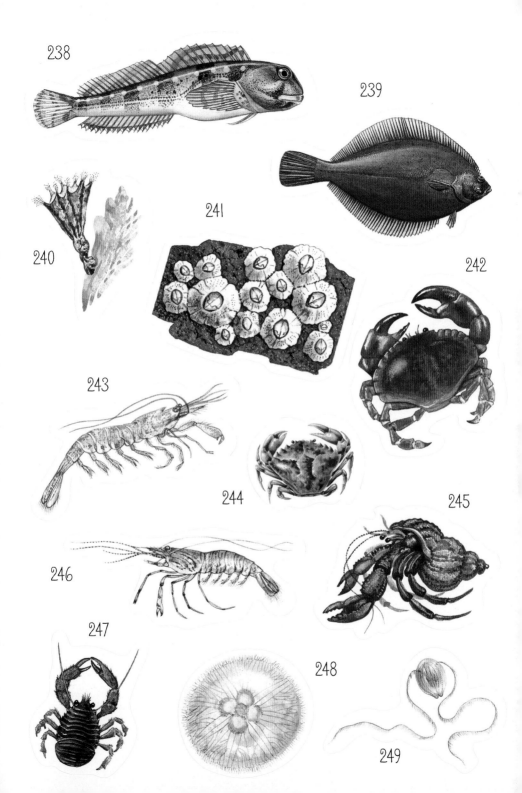

238

239

240

241

242

243

244

245

246

247

248

249

250

251

252

254

255

253

257

258

256

259

260

261

262

263

264

265

266

267

268

269

Eggs on
water plants

270

271

272

273

274

275

276

—Saddle

277

278

279

280

281

282